# The Secrets of
# Vaccination

Sarah Blackmore

Published in association with The Basic Skills Agency

## Hodder & Stoughton
A MEMBER OF THE HODDER HEADLINE GROUP

**Acknowledgements**

Cover: © Hulton Getty

Photos: p 3 Popperfoto; p 5 Eye of Science/Science Photo Library; pp 15, 17, 20 Mary Evans Picture Library; p 25 Saturn Stills/Science Photo Library; p 27 Hawk Morgan/Science Photo Library

Every effort has been made to trace copyright holders of material reproduced in this book. Any rights not acknowledged will be acknowledged in subsequent printings if notice is given to the publisher.

Orders; please contact Bookpoint Ltd, 39 Milton Park, Abingdon, Oxon OX14 4TD. Telephone: (44) 01235 400414, Fax: (44) 01235 400454. Lines are open from 9.00–6.00, Monday to Saturday, with a 24 hour message answering service. Email address: orders@bookpoint.co.uk

*British Library Cataloguing in Publication Data*
A catalogue record for this title is available from the British Library

ISBN 0 340 77648 X

First published 2000
Impression number    10 9 8 7 6 5 4 3 2 1
Year                 2005 2004 2003 2002 2001 2000

Copyright © 1999 NTC/Contemporary Publishing Group, Inc.

Adapted for the Livewire series by Sarah Blackmore

Typeset by GreenGate Publishing Services, Tonbridge, Kent.
Printed in Great Britain for Hodder and Stoughton Educational, a division of Hodder Headline Plc, 338 Euston Road, London NW1 3BH, by Redwood Books, Trowbridge, Wilts

# Contents

In the 18th Century there was a disease that killed thousands.

Edward Jenner (on the cover) helped to find a cure to fight the disease.

Read on to find out more.

# 1 Monster Disease

Have you ever been scared of monsters?
Maybe you were scared of monsters
when you were younger.
Have you ever seen a terrifying monster?
Perhaps you saw one in a horror film.

There was once a monster that scared everybody.
It was a speckled monster.
It scared people living in the 18th Century.

It was a killer monster.
Each year it killed more than 1 million people.

Most of its victims were children.
The monster attacked anyone.
It even killed five kings.

What was it?
What was this monster?

Its name was smallpox.
Many people called it 'the Pox'.

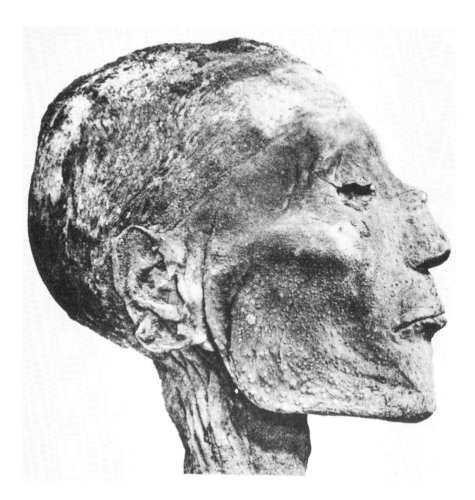

The mummified face of an Egyptian Pharaoh. Smallpox scars can be seen on his skin.

# 2 The Pox

The pox was a disease.
People could catch it in different ways.
It was very infectious.

It could infect people through the air.
It could infect people when they touched each other.
It could hang on clothes or bed sheets
and infect people when they touched them.

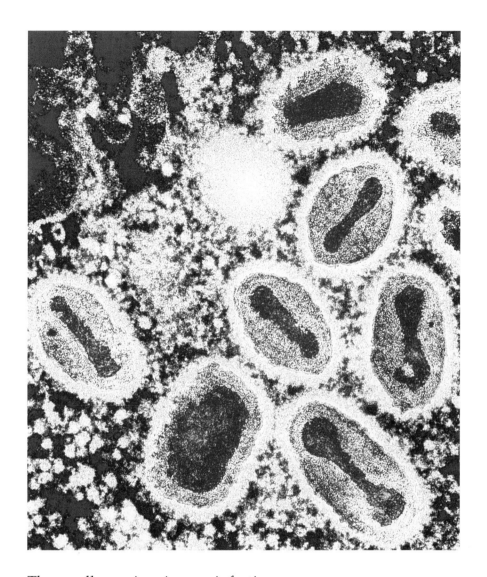

The smallpox virus is very infectious.

What did the pox do to people?
The first sign of the pox might be a headache.
You would also have a high temperature
and your body would ache.

Just like flu to start with
but it got worse.
Much worse.

In a short time, the speckles would appear.
Red spots on your face.
Red spots on your arms and legs.

The spots swelled up into watery blisters.
If the blisters began to bleed you would die quickly.
If the blisters scabbed over you would get better.

If you were lucky enough to live
you would have marks from the spots.
Ugly marks on your face and body.
Sometimes the pox left people blind.

# 3  Spread of the Disease

Smallpox killed people all over the world.
It spread between countries as people travelled.
For over 2,000 years it infected and killed.
In the 1500s it killed about 3.5 million people
in South America.
It did this in just two years.

This monster was a killer.
Doctors tried to find a cure.
They had to find some way
of slowing the monster down.
They wanted to find a way to stop it.

# 4 Finding a Cure

Doctors watched people to see what happened
when they had the pox.
They noticed that if a person lived,
he or she never got the pox again.
It seemed that getting the pox meant
you could not get it again.

This gave doctors an idea.
They infected people on purpose
with a mild dose of the pox.
They did this
by taking liquid from the smallpox blisters.
They injected the liquid into people's skins.

Some people then had a mild case of the pox.
They were very happy.
Why?
Well, a mild case of pox did not kill them.
It meant that they would not get the pox again.

The doctors were not sure about how much
they should inject into people.
Many people got too much.
It killed them.

# 5 Edward Jenner

One doctor knew all about smallpox.
His name was Edward Jenner.
He was English.
He lived over 200 years ago.

Edward Jenner had worked out
something really interesting.
There was one group of people
who never seemed to get the pox.
They were people who worked with cows.

Edward Jenner knew all about smallpox.

Milkmaids often got something called cowpox.
This was disease from cows.
It did not kill people.

Milkmaids got blisters from cowpox
but they did not seem to catch smallpox.

Milkmaids got cowpox from cows. They did not seem to catch smallpox.

Jenner worked out that
having cowpox protected people against smallpox.
This gave him an idea.
If he gave people a mild dose of cowpox
it might protect them against smallpox.
If it did, it would be a vaccine.

On 14 May 1796, Jenner tried an experiment.
He found a milkmaid who had cowpox.
She had cowpox blisters on her fingers.

Jenner took some liquid from the blisters.
He then injected it into an eight-year-old boy.
The boy's name was James.

Edward Jenner did an experiment. He injected a boy with some liquid from cowpox blisters.

In a short time James had a mild case of cowpox.
He had one small blister, but nothing else.

Six weeks later, Jenner injected James with smallpox.
Everybody watched and waited.
Would James get the pox?

Was Jenner right?
Had he got it wrong?

# 6  Finding a Vaccine

Jenner was right.
James did not get the pox.
Cowpox had protected him from smallpox.

Edward Jenner had discovered a vaccine.

In time other doctors used the cowpox vaccine.
It worked,
but the smallpox monster still killed many people.
Why?

Well, there was not enough cowpox vaccine
for everyone.
Cowpox was not that common.
Also the vaccine was difficult to keep.
It was easily damaged by heat.

The pox could not be stopped.
It went on killing for over 100 years
after Jenner's work.

# 7  A New Vaccine

At last in the 1930s,
a much better vaccine was developed.
The new vaccine did not spoil in the heat.
It did not cost too much to make.
It could be used to stop the pox.

Doctors and nurses gave the vaccine
to children everywhere.
By 1980 smallpox had been stopped.

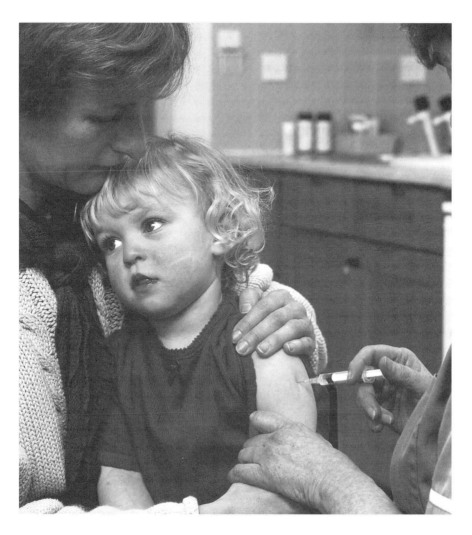

In the 1930s a better vaccine was made. This was given to children all over the world.

Are you scared of monsters?
You need not be scared of the speckled monster.
Thanks to the work of Edward Jenner and others.

There are still other monsters.
Other diseases that kill many people.

The work of Edward Jenner
helped people understand more about vaccines.
Many vaccines have been developed
to protect us against diseases.
A lot of work is still being done.
Work to develop new and better vaccines.

Today scientists are working to develop new vaccines for other diseases.